The C-A-R-E Project
Conflict And Responsibility Education

Written by Dr. Gerri Holden

Illustrated by Darcy Tom

Teaching & Learning Company

1204 Buchanan St., P.O. Box 10
Carthage, IL 62321-0010

This book belongs to

_____

Cover design by Sara King

Copyright © 2001, Teaching & Learning Company

ISBN No. 1-57310-305-5

Printing No. 987654321

Teaching & Learning Company
1204 Buchanan St., P.O. Box 10
Carthage, IL 62321-0010

Table of Contents

Dear Teacher or Parent,

After you've settled the issues and settled the kids, how do you teach them to be caring and considerate friends? *The C-A-R-E Project* focuses on character building, conflict management, life skills and problem solving. Since we are all concerned about the negative behaviors that our young are displaying, I wrote this book to help teach children to get along with their classmates and their families and to respect one another's differences. It will teach children how to take responsibility for their own behavior, how to show respect and how to be resourceful—in other words, how to find new solutions to old problems. It was also written with you, the teacher, in mind. This book has everything you need to teach conflict management and responsibility education. You will find games, puzzles, lots of songs and other activities to help kids focus on responsible behavior. Classroom posters, bulletin boards and teacher-friendly forms are also included. The objectives were especially written from a constructivist model and were chosen to ensure that critical thinking skills would be encouraged. Most of the lessons will allow students to use prior knowledge and analytical skills in addition to allowing for self-reflection regarding responsible behavior. Feel free to add objectives or revise objectives in the Bloom's Taxonomy charts.

I have also attempted to incorporate your children's multiple intelligences in practically every lesson. Of course, you can add activities that would further enhance the multiple intelligences in your classroom. Finally, all the activities are easy to use and your kids will especially love "The C-A-R-E Kids Song." Mine did.

Best of luck to you,

Gerri

Dr. Gerri Holden

Lesson Plans
Conflict Resolution and Character Education

Bloom's Taxonomy of the Cognitive Domain

Behavior	Lesson Objectives—Unit 1	
	Lesson 1 **What Are Conflicts?**	**Lesson 2** **Reasons Conflicts Escalate**
Knowledge To recall, recognize, acquire, identify, define; the focus is on remembering.	Students will be able to define the words *conflict, resolve, violence* and *problem*.	Students will be able to define the following: *alone, rage, rejection, revenge, self-control* and *temper*.
Comprehension To translate, transform, put in own words, rephrase, restate; this is the first level of understanding.	Students will be able to explain two causes of conflicts.	Students will be able to explain in their own words why conflicts escalate and become violent.
Application To generalize, choose, develop, organize, use, transfer, restructure, classify; ability to use information in new situations.		Students will be able to discuss a situation where they lost their temper.
Analysis To distinguish, detect, classify, disseminate, categorize, deduce, contrast, compare.		
Synthesis To write, tell, produce, constitute, transmit, originate, design, formulate; ability to put elements together to form a new whole.	Students will be able to write about a conflict they had at home or school and tell why they think the conflict started.	Using the Think & Write section of the lesson, students will write their understanding of the term *making a mountain out of a molehill*.
Evaluation To argue, validate, assess, appraise, decide; judgments based on criteria of value or worth.		

Lesson Plans

Conflict Resolution and Character Education

Bloom's Taxonomy of the Cognitive Domain

Behavior	**Lesson Objectives—Unit 1**	
	Lesson 3 **Review**	
Knowledge To recall, recognize, acquire, identify, define; the focus is on remembering.	Students will be able to list and define the three reasons why conflicts turn violent.	
Comprehension To translate, transform, put in own words, rephrase, restate; this is the first level of understanding.		
Application To generalize, choose, develop, organize, use, transfer, restructure, classify; ability to use information in new situations.		
Analysis To distinguish, detect, classify, disseminate, categorize, deduce, contrast, compare.		
Synthesis To write, tell, produce, constitute, transmit, originate, design, formulate; ability to put elements together to form a new whole.	Students will be able to write an essay using their conflict maps.	
Evaluation To argue, validate, assess, appraise, decide; judgments based on criteria of value or worth.	Students will be able to evaluate the causes of conflict and what determines whether they will escalate.	

Behavior	Lesson Objectives—Unit 2	
	Lesson 1 Responsibility	**Lesson 2** Respect
Knowledge To recall, recognize, acquire, identify, define; the focus is on remembering.	Students will be able to identify the three Rs that make conflicts easy to resolve.	
Comprehension To translate, transform, put in own words, rephrase, restate; this is the first level of understanding.		Students will be able to explain and discuss the rights of others.
Application To generalize, choose, develop, organize, use, transfer, restructure, classify; ability to use information in new situations.	Students will be able to list two ways they can show responsibility at home and at school.	Students will be able to demonstrate ways to show respect for other people's space and property.
Analysis To distinguish, detect, classify, disseminate, categorize, deduce, contrast, compare.		Students will be able to explain how showing respect reduces conflicts.
Synthesis To write, tell, produce, constitute, transmit, originate, design, formulate; ability to put elements together to form a new whole.		Students will be able to state ways they can effectively listen to others.
Evaluation To argue, validate, assess, appraise, decide; judgments based on criteria of value or worth.		

Lesson Plans
Conflict Resolution and Character Education

Bloom's Taxonomy of the Cognitive Domain

| | Lesson Objectives—Unit 2 | |
Behavior	**Lesson 3** **Resourceful**	**Lesson 4** **Review**
Knowledge To recall, recognize, acquire, identify, define; the focus is on remembering.	Students will be able to define the terms *compromise*, *reasonable* and *remedy*.	Students will be able to know and explain the acronym C.I.A.
Comprehension To translate, transform, put in own words, rephrase, restate; this is the first level of understanding.	Students will be able to explain two new ways to resolve conflicts through being a good friend.	Students will be able to explain what it means to be resourceful.
Application To generalize, choose, develop, organize, use, transfer, restructure, classify; ability to use information in new situations.		Students will be able to demonstrate conflict management skills using a phone conversation simulation.
Analysis To distinguish, detect, classify, disseminate, categorize, deduce, contrast, compare.		
Synthesis To write, tell, produce, constitute, transmit, originate, design, formulate; ability to put elements together to form a new whole.		
Evaluation To argue, validate, assess, appraise, decide; judgments based on criteria of value or worth.		Students will be able to discuss ways of resolving conflict through respect, responsibility and resourcefulness.

Incorporating the Multiple Intelligences

Multiple Intelligence

Unit and Lesson	Word Smart	Music Smart	Numbers Smart	Body Smart	People Smart	Self-Smart	Picture Smart
Unit 1: The Causes of Conflicts							
Lesson 1	X	X	X		X		X
Lesson 2	X	X	X				X
Lesson 3	X		X			X	X
Unit 2: Solutions to Conflicts: The Three Rs of Character							
Lesson 1	X	X		X	X		
Lesson 2	X	X			X		
Lesson 3			X		X		
Lesson 4	X				X		X
Teacher Helpers	Story Starters Word Strips While You Are Waiting Shape Book		Math Helpers	C-A-R-E Game	Folder Full of Friendly Facts Shape Book	Story Starters Folder Full of Friendly Facts Shape Book	Posters

The chart shows by Xs areas that include a particular multiple intelligence. You can decide to do supplemental activities that would embrace those intelligences not represented in a particular lesson. For example, you may allow Self-Smart students to keep a special journal. Students can record their thoughts about the assignments, about friendships, problems, etc. You may allow Picture Smart learners to draw more pictures. They may also take a survey of favorite things to do with friends and then make a graph. Another example would be to allow Picture Smart students to help design bulletin boards. The Teacher Helpers have a variety of projects that can be used as is or adapted to suit the needs of your class.

Teacher Directions
Unit 1: The Causes of Conflicts

Objectives

Students will be able to:
1. Define the words *conflict, resolve, violence* and *problem*.
2. Explain at least two causes of conflict.
3. Write about a conflict they had at home or school and tell why they think the conflict started.

Vocabulary

conflict   violence
resolve   problem

Activities

Word Webs
Vocabulary
Story Starters–Pre and Post Assessment
Word Scramble
"The C-A-R-E Kids Song"

Teacher Directions

Unit 1, Lesson 1: What Are Conflicts?

Word Webs

Write a word web on the chalkboard. Discuss with the students the definition of *conflicts* and why they exist. Ask the following questions:

1. What is a conflict? (Do a word web.)
   A conflict is a disagreement between two or more people. Conflicts are a normal, natural part of life.

Word Web

- Put the word web on the board or overhead projector.

- Discuss the words with your students.

- Write down the students' responses.

- Let the students copy the answers onto their word webs. (Reproducible on page 24.)

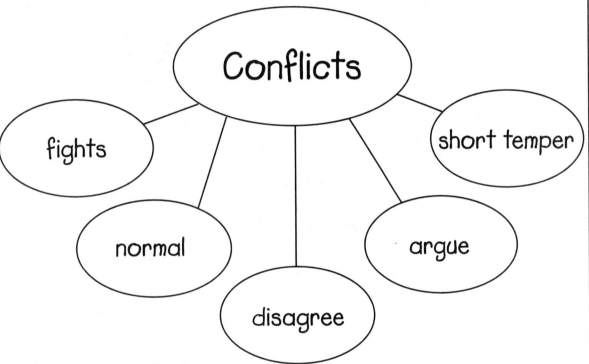

1. What causes conflicts?

   Answers will vary. Try brainstorming. Tell the students that often times disagreements, jealousy, intolerance, short tempers, differences of opinion and misunderstandings cause conflicts.

2. Who do we have conflicts with? (Do a word web.)

   Answers will vary. Conflicts are between one other person or a group of people. Conflicts can also be with friends, neighbors, brothers, sisters, classmates, other family members and teachers.

Word Web

- Put the word web on the board or overhead projector

- Discuss the words with your students.

- Write down the students' responses.

- Let students copy the answers onto their word webs. (Reproducible on page 25.)

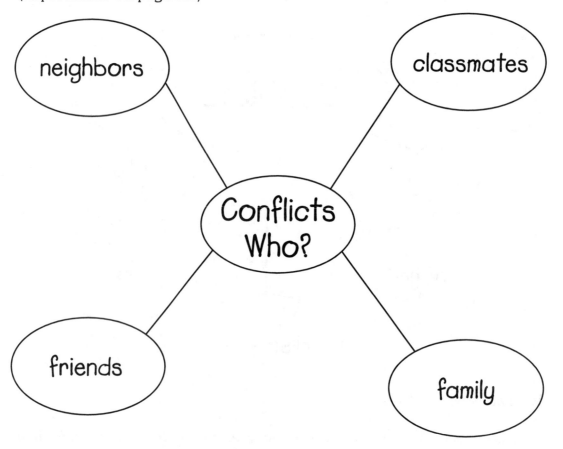

3. What are some of the things people do during a conflict?

Answers will vary. Tell the students that many people react to conflict in different ways. Some will show violence such as fighting. Others may scream, pout, run, not speak to one another, stop being friends or cry. Tell the students they will learn character skills that will teach them better ways to handle their conflicts.

Vocabulary

Write the vocabulary words on the board. Go over the vocabulary words with the students. Define each word. After the discussion on conflict, let the students put their words in alphabetical order and in sentences. Do the Word Scramble. (Reproducible on page 29.)

Conflict: a disagreement between two people or a group of people.
Resolve: to bring something to a successful end; to change something; to make everything okay again.
Violence: hurting someone; fighting; violence can be verbal or nonverbal and includes threats and intimidation.
Problem: a situation or person who causes us to be upset or worried.

Story Starters and Word Scramble

Allow students to work on the Story Starters and Word Scramble as seatwork or as homework. Use the Story Starters as pre and post assessments. (Reproducibles on pages 27-29.)

The C-A-R-E Kids Song

"The C-A-R-E Kids Song" will be an important theme throughout this curriculum. Teach the children to sing it now. Allow them many opportunities during the school year to sing the song. This is a fun song. Your students will love it. My students made up their own tune. (Reproducible on page 30.)
(If you are totally stuck for a melody, you can fit these words to "Turkey in the Straw." Spell out C-A-R-E, and repeat the first verse at the end.)

Unit 1, Lesson 2: Reasons Conflicts Escalate

Objectives

Students will be able to:
1. Define *alone*, *rage*, *rejection*, *revenge*, *self-control* and *temper*.
2. Explain in their own words why conflicts escalate and become violent.
3. Discuss a situation where they lost their temper.
4. Using the Think & Write section of the lesson, write their understanding of the term *making a mountain out of a molehill*.

Visual Organizer and Vocabulary

alone	revenge	rage
self-control	rejection	temper

Activities

Visual Organizer
Vocabulary
Think & Write–Rejection

Think & Write–Rage
Think & Write–Revenge (Role Play)

Teacher Directions

1. Ask students to tell you what they think causes conflicts to become violent. Their answers will vary. Allow them to brainstorm.
2. Tell students that there are three words that all begin with the letter R. Each word is a reason why conflicts become violent. See if the students can guess the words. The three Rs are: *Rage, Rejection* and *Revenge*. Discuss each of these words in detail.

Give each student a copy of the Visual Organizer. (Reproducible on page 31.) Discuss with them the words and their various meanings. Let them record their responses in the appropriate boxes. Use synonyms (for example, the word *rage* also means "mad, angry or furious"). Then have the students pick one of the words and write several sentences about the word. Younger children can draw pictures. Discuss with the children how problems escalate.

Visual Organizer

Rage	Rejection	Revenge
mad	lonely	mean
angry	unhappy	hate
furious	separate	get back
temper tantrum	alone	pay back
holler	no friends	retaliation
yell	teasing	retort
scream	not being included	
fight	feeling unwanted	
self-control		

Think & Write

Summarize what the students have learned so far. Tell them that conflicts become violent when people loose self-control (rage), feel unwanted (rejection) or try to get even (revenge). Discuss the idiom: *making a mountain out of a mole-hill*. Ask the students to write a paragraph on what this idiom means. Use the other *Think & Write* exercises in this lesson. (Reproducibles on pages 33-36.) You may use them for extra work, seatwork, homework or as a part of your class writing assignments. These exercises work well with the writing process.

Unit 1, Lesson 3: Review

Students will be able to:
1. List and define the three reasons why conflicts turn violent.
2. Evaluate the causes of conflicts and what determines whether they will escalate.
3. Write an essay using a conflict map.

Vocabulary (Review from Lessons 1 and 2)

alone	resolve
conflict	revenge
problem	self-control
rage	temper
rejection	violence

Activities

Vocabulary	Missing Vowels
Conflict Map	Vocabulary Search (Test)
Word Search	Think & Write–Essay Question

Teacher Directions (Reproducibles on pages 37-42.)

1. Review lessons one and two. Go over the vocabulary words. Ask students to volunteer to define the words.
2. Review the three Rs that cause conflicts to become violent.
3. Do a conflict map. A conflict map is the same as a story map.
4. Think & Write: Allow the students to write their essays using their conflict map.
5. Allow the students to work on the various activities of this unit as independent activities, small group activities or homework.

Unit 2: Solutions to Conflicts
Management Strategies
Unit 2, Lesson 1: Responsibility

Objectives

Students will be able to:
1. Identify the three Rs that make conflicts easy to resolve.
2. List two ways they can show responsibility at home and at school.
3. Differentiate between behavior that lacks self-control and behavior that shows respect.

Vocabulary

responsibility   resourceful   respect

Activities

Visual Organizer   Be a Busy "Buddy"
Responsibility Test   Story Starters
"Be Your Best" Rap

Story: *Alexander and the Terrible, Horrible, No Good, Very Bad Day* by Judith Viorst, Aladdin Paperbacks, 1987, reissue edition. Also available on video from Golden Books (VHS), 1999.

Teacher Directions

Discuss the words *responsibility*, *respect* and *resourceful*. Explain to your students that they will learn these excellent character traits in this unit. These character skills will help them to solve their conflicts. Give each student a copy of the Visual Organizer. (Reproducible on page 44.) Discuss with them the words and their various meanings. Let them record their responses in the appropriate boxes. Use synonyms. Then have the students pick one of the words and write several sentences about the word. Younger children can draw pictures. Discuss with the children ways to show responsibility, respect and resourcefulness at school and at home.

Visual Organizer

Responsibility	Respect	Resourceful
obligation	considerate	knowing a better way for doing something
trustworthy	kind	skillful
reliable	listens to others	creative
deserving credit	polite	creative
careful	cares and shares	knowing good remedies

The first lesson is on responsibility. For fun, put the students into groups and see how many words they make from the word *responsibility*. The following is a partial list.

pen	ten	son	tore
bless	sore	be	rip
stop	ripe	probe	person
tin	yes	rib	no
on	one	pose	nose
rose	rosy	son	ton
oil	boil	toil	soil
sob	rob	spit	it
is	best	rest	nest

Next, discuss the following two major areas of responsibility.

Self-Control

We have bad days. Read the storybook *Alexander and the Terrible, Horrible, No Good, Very Bad Day* by Judith Viorst. Do a story map or a book report. Discuss with children their bad days. Get them to talk about their feelings and what positive things they can do to feel better. Let them complete the story starter: The Worst Day I Ever Had Was When . . . (Note: You can do this orally or have the students write or illustrate their answers.) Tell the students that taking self-control means that I am responsible for my behavior. Emphasize that they are only responsible for their own behavior, not someone else's. Tell students that they cannot change others; they can only change themselves. It is not their fault if others choose to fight. However, they must not imitate that behavior. Tell the students if they do not control themselves, other people or situations will control them. Go over the Responsibility Test on page 45. Discuss each of the 10 points, then allow the students to circle their answers.

Good Citizens

We are responsible to people and the environment. We must learn to be peace-makers. Assign four students to be "rappers." Have them to learn the "Be Your Best" Rap on page 46. Have them to perform it before the class. Or, let the whole class learn the rap and say it together. Use your imagination on this one and have lots of fun. Next, teach students that good citizens are not busybodies (people who keep fights alive). Do the worksheets on pages 47-48.

Busy Buddy

This is a good way to reinforce the concept of minding one's own business. Discuss what it means to be a busybody and how being one can cause severe problems. Talk about how busybodies like to keep fights and arguments brewing. Then discuss with the children what it is like to be a "busy buddy." Read the short description, complete the comprehension questions and then complete the cloze sheet.

Story Starter

Tell the students to write how to be responsible when faced with a conflict.

Unit 2, Lesson 2: Respect

Objectives

Students will be able to:
1. Explain and discuss the rights of others.
2. Demonstrate ways to show respect for other people's space and property.
3. Explain how showing respect reduces conflicts.
4. State ways they can effectively listen to others.

Vocabulary

care

celebrate

cooperate

difference

listen

peaceful

Activities

Story Starter: Respect

Poetry Corner: "Code of Conduct"

Bulletin Boards

Handwriting Practice

Celebrate the Difference (Choral Reading)

Research Project: The Hands

Choral Reading

"Good Manners" Song

Teacher Directions

Story Starter: Respect

Complete the Story Starter on page 50 in class or assign for homework.

Poetry Corner: "Code of Conduct"

The purpose of the poetry corner is to reinforce respect. This lesson on rhyme can also be used to practice handwriting. Use the code signs on pages 92-94 in the Teacher Helper section to help reinforce this concept. Laminate the signs and hang them in full view of your students. Let the students recite the code daily. Then pass out the student's copy of the signs. Allow them to write the Code of Conduct and color the picture.

Choral Reading

Make sufficient copies of the choral reading on page 56 for each child. Allow the students to practice.

Bulletin Board

Make a bulletin board "Celebrate the Difference." Have students write papers about themselves and how they are different from others. Have younger children draw pictures. Hang pictures or stories on the bulletin board.
(Note: See the Bulletin Board section on pages 95-100.)

Research Project: The Hands

Use the worksheet on page 57 to teach research skills. Use the assignments as they are or modify them to suit your class level.

"Good Manners" Song

Teach the song on page 58 to your students and let them sing it daily.

Unit 2, Lesson 3: Resourceful

Objectives

Students will be able to:
1. Define the terms *compromise, reasonable* and *remedy*.
2. Explain two new ways to resolve conflicts through being a good friend.

Vocabulary

compromise
reasonable
friendship
remedy

Activities

Let's Talk

A Is for Friendship

Think & Write–Friendship Sayings

Think & Write–Master Scientist

Teacher Directions

Tell the students they are promoted to CIAs (Conflict Intelligence Agent) because they know so much about conflicts and how to solve them. They are now responsible for finding reasonable remedies to conflicts. Give them the cover assignment sheet: Reasonable Remedies–CIA Assignment Sheet on page 59.

Assignment 1: Let's Talk

Give the students the packet and let them complete it. You may use this assignment for a bulletin board display. (See Bulletin Boards in the Teacher Helpers section.)

Are You Listening?

Respect also requires that we use good listening skills. Discuss with students how to listen to each other without interruption. Let them practice in groups. Pay particular attention to the Code of Conduct rhyme for this section.

Assignment 2: A Is for Friendship

Let the students complete the A Is for Friendship assignment sheet on page 63. Then ask them to think of B words for friendship such as: *best, buddy, beautiful, brainy, brilliant, brother,* etc. Finally, have students look up their vocabulary words in the dictionary. Let them work in teams. Then allow them to put their vocabulary words into sentences.

Assignment 3: Friendship Sayings

For extra classwork or for homework, let the students pick one of the Friendship Sayings on page 64 and write about it.

Assignment 4: Master Scientist

Tell the students they are all mad scientists (who happen to be very friendly). Let them invent a tonic or formula for developing friendships or solving problems. Use the worksheet in this unit. At the end of all five assignments, staple the worksheets together to the cover assignment sheet.

Unit 2, Lesson 4: Review

Objectives

The student will be able to:

1. Know and explain the acronym CIA (Conflict Intelligence Agent).
2. Explain what it means to be resourceful.
3. Demonstrate conflict management skills by using a phone conversation simulation.
4. Discuss ways of resolving conflicts through respect, responsibility and resourcefulness.

Vocabulary (Review of Lessons 1-3)

care	friendship	remedy
celebrate	listen	resourceful
compromise	peaceful	respect
cooperate	reasonable	responsibility
difference		

Activities

C-A-R-E Contract
Presentation
Special Assignment–C-A-R-E Meeting
Nameplate
Think & Write–What Have You Learned?

Poem: "The New Kid on the Block" by Jack Prelutsky, from *The New Kid on the Block*, Greenwillow, 1984.

Teacher Directions

This is the final review section. Make a copy of the C-A-R-E Contract on page 66 for each student. Have them sign their contracts. Do the activities in this section.

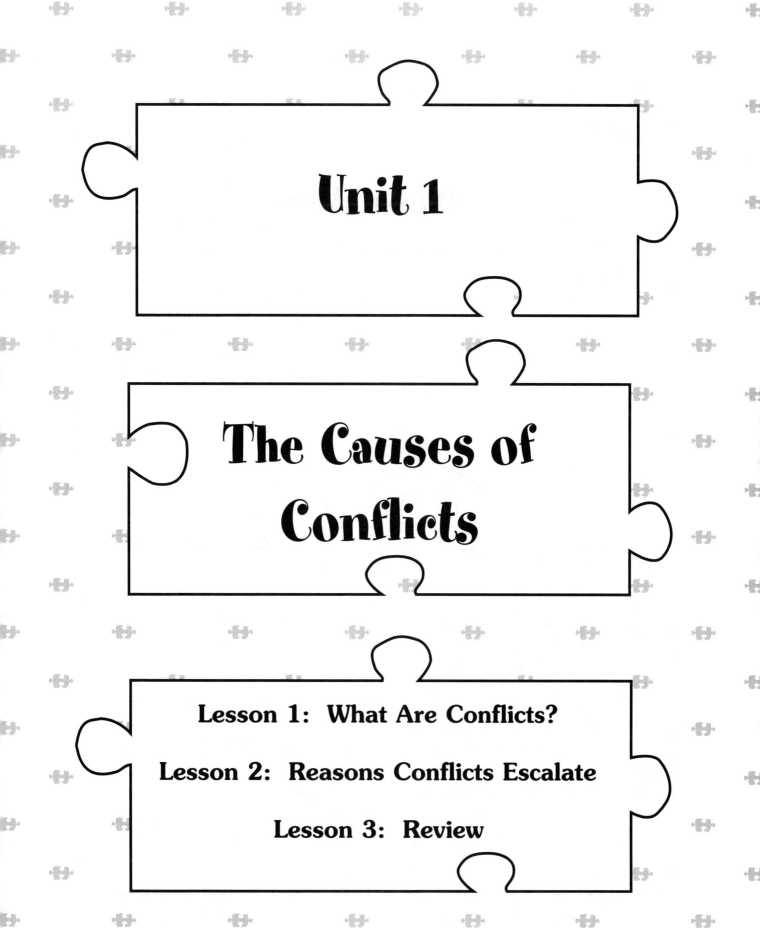

Unit 1

The Causes of Conflicts

Lesson 1: What Are Conflicts?

Lesson 2: Reasons Conflicts Escalate

Lesson 3: Review

Name: _____

Word Web

Listen to your teacher. Copy the words about conflict in the ovals.

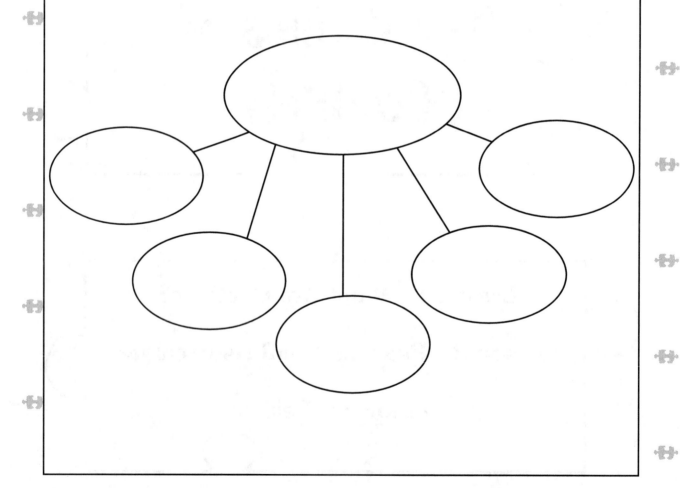

Name: _____

Word Web

Listen to your teacher. Fill in the ovals.

Unit 1, Lesson 1

Name: _____

Vocabulary

Write your vocabulary words in alphabetical order.
Then use each word in a sentence.

Word Bank	
conflict	violence
resolve	problem

ABC Order

1. _____

2. _____

3. _____

4. _____

Write four sentences using each word.

_____

_____

_____

_____

_____

Unit 1, Lesson 1

Name: _____

Story Starter

When I get very angry, the good things I can do are . . .

_____

_____

_____

_____

_____

_____

_____

_____

_____

_____

_____

_____

_____

_____

_____

Name: _____

Story Starter

Things That Bug Me

Write about all the things that make you mad or "bug" you.
What is a good way to handle those problems from now on?

_____

_____

_____

_____

_____

_____

_____

_____

_____

_____

_____

_____

Name: _____

Word Scramble

Unscramble the words below to see your new vocabulary words.

1. cltnoicf _____

2. vseelro _____

3. cineoevl _____

4. lrbpoem _____

The C-A-R-E Kids Song

We're the C-A-R-E kids,
Do you want to know why?
We C-A-R-E about others,
We help the other guy.

We're happy and we're proud,
If you know what we mean.
We don't follow the crowd,
We do our own thing.

When you help someone,
They will help you someday.
That's the way it goes,
Turnabout is fair play.

We're the C-A-R-E kids,
'Cause we have a caring heart.
If you want to be the best,
Showing love is always smart.

If you want to make a difference,
And you want to make a friend,
Just be a C-A-R-E kid,
That's the only way you'll win!

Name: _____

Visual Organizer

Listen to your teacher. Fill in the spaces under each word.

Rage	Rejection	Revenge

Vocabulary

Rage: Anger that is very upsetting; being furious; to lose self-control.

Rejection: Not being accepted or included; to be pushed away.

Revenge: To pay back an injury; to get even.

Name: _____

Vocabulary

Write your vocabulary words in alphabetical order.
Then use each word in a sentence.

Word Bank

rage	alone
revenge	temper
rejection	self-control

ABC Order

1. _____   4. _____

2. _____   5. _____

3. _____   6. _____

Write a sentence using each word.

_____

_____

_____

_____

_____

_____

TLC10305 Copyright © Teaching & Learning Company, Carthage, IL 62321-0010

Think & Write-Rejection

Rejection means "feeling that you do not belong or feeling that you are unwanted."

Look at the following two assignments. Pick one and write about it. Remember the writing process. First think about what you want to write about. Then make a draft. Let your teacher or a friend read your draft. Make corrections or edit the draft. Make sure you have made all the changes. Write your final story in your best handwriting and turn it in to the teacher.

Assignment 1

Tell about a time that you felt rejected. How did you feel or what did you do?

Assignment 2

Anna wanted to play basketball. However, no one picked her for their team. How do you think Anna feels? What do you think Anna should do?

Name: _____

Think & Write-Rage

Rage is when a person does not show self-control. It means that our anger is severe. When we feel rage, it means we can lose our tempers.

What do you think people should do when they get very angry? What could they do to keep from feeling rage?

Write your answer to the questions below.

_____

_____

_____

_____

_____

_____

_____

_____

_____

_____

_____

Name: _____

Think & Write-Revenge (Role Play)

To get revenge means to get even with someone. When we seek revenge instead of resolutions, problems usually just get bigger. Read the story below. Tell what you think will happen to Sonny and Jake.

> Sonny thought that Jake had taken his pencil. Jake said he found it on the playground. Sonny became angry when Jake would not give the pencil to him. The next day, Sonny decided to take Jake's new eraser.

What do you think will happen next? What will Jake do? Do you think Sonny made a good or bad decision? What other decision could Sonny make?

_____

_____

_____

_____

_____

_____

_____

_____

_____

_____

_____

Name: _____

Think & Write

Have you ever heard the expression: *Don't fight fire with fire. Fight fire with water!*

What do you think it means?

In the previous story Sonny wanted to fight fire with fire. He thought that someone had taken something that belonged to him, so he decided to take something of value that belonged to someone else. Of course, this just made the fight bigger.

Think of situations you know about where students sought revenge instead of resolutions. Think of your classroom, the lunchroom or the playground. Describe the conflict. What are some better ways to handle that situation? In other words, how could the students have put water on the fire to put it out, instead of adding fire to make it worse? Record your assignment below.

Describe a conflict.

_____

_____

_____

_____

Fire Fighting Technique.

_____

_____

_____

_____

Name: _____

Vocabulary

Write your vocabulary words in alphabetical order.
Then look up the words in a dictionary. Write a short definition for each.

Word Bank

conflict	resolve	violence	rage
revenge	problem	alone	temper
rejection	self-control		

ABC Order

1. _____   6. _____

2. _____   7. _____

3. _____   8. _____

4. _____   9. _____

5. _____   10. _____

Definitions (Use your dictionary.)

alone: _____

conflict: _____

problem: _____

rage: _____

rejection: _____

resolve: _____

revenge: _____

self-control: _____

temper: _____

violence: _____

Name: _____

Conflict Map

Answer the questions below.
The five important questions are "who, what, where, how and why."

WHAT is a conflict? (definition)

WHY do conflicts happen? (cause)

WHO do we have conflicts with? (people involved)

_____   _____

_____   _____

_____   _____

WHERE do many conflicts take place? (home, school, playground)

HOW do conflicts turn violent?
(Name the three Rs.)

R_____

R_____

R_____

Name: _____

Word Search

Using the word bank, find the hidden words in the puzzle.
Look across and down.

```
N  S  P  R  O  B  L  E  M
R  E  J  E  C  T  I  O  N
E  L  O  V  E  F  R  Q  T
S  F  A  E  O  I  V  S  L
O  C  O  N  F  L  I  C  T
L  O  R  G  E  R  O  N  E
V  N  A  E  K  A  L  U  M
E  T  G  A  N  G  E  R  P
N  R  A  G  E  R  N  E  E
D  O  R  E  J  E  C  B  R
A  L  O  N  E  E  E  S  T
```

Word Bank

violence	self-control
rejection	problem
conflict	temper
revenge	resolve
rage	anger
alone	agree

Name: _____

Missing Vowels

Fill in the missing vowel (a, e, i, o, u) for each vocabulary word.

1. v _ _ l _ nc _
2. c _ nfl _ ct
3. r _ g _
4. p r _ b l _ m
5. t _ mp _ r
6. r _ s _ lv _
7. r _ j _ ct _ _ n
8. r _ v _ ng _
9. _ l _ n _
10. s _ lf - c _ ntr _ l

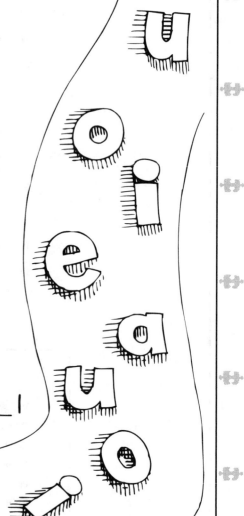

Unit 1, Lesson 3

Name: _____

Vocabulary Search (Test)

_____ 1. a disagreement between two or more people

_____ 2. to bring something to a successful end

_____ 3. hurting someone; fighting

_____ 4. being very angry; losing self-control

_____ 5. not being accepted or included

_____ 6. to pay back an injury; to get even

_____ 7. a situation or person who causes us to be upset or worried

a. rejection

b. violence

c. revenge

d. resolve

e. conflict

f. problem

g. rage

Name: _____

Think & Write-Essay Question

What is a conflict? Write about why we have conflicts. Tell about the three reasons that conflicts turn violent. You may use your conflict map.

_____

_____

_____

_____

_____

_____

_____

_____

_____

_____

_____

_____

_____

_____

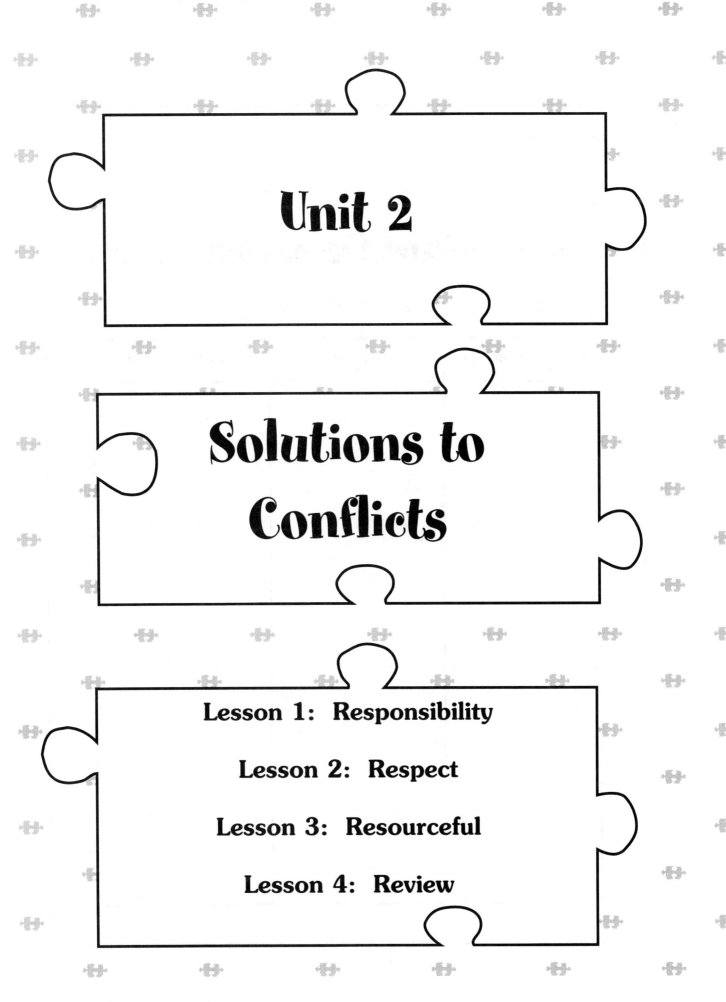

Unit 2

Solutions to Conflicts

Lesson 1: Responsibility

Lesson 2: Respect

Lesson 3: Resourceful

Lesson 4: Review

Unit 2, Lesson 1

Name: _____

Visual Organizer

Listen to your teacher. Fill in the spaces under each word.

Responsibility	Respect	Resourceful

Unit 2, Lesson 1

Name: _____

Responsibility Test

Take the following short test. Circle *yes* or *no*.
You get one point for each "yes" answer.

	Circle one	
1. I admit when I am wrong.	Yes	No
2. I say, "I'm sorry" when I make a mistake.	Yes	No
3. I practice good manners by saying "please."	Yes	No
4. I do not blame others for my mistakes.	Yes	No
5. I tell the whole truth.	Yes	No
6. I try to care and share.	Yes	No
7. I do not **start** fights.	Yes	No
8. I care about other people's feelings.	Yes	No
9. I try to find peaceful solutions to problems.	Yes	No
10. I always do my best.	Yes	No
Total number of points: _____		

"Be Your Best" Rap

Rapper 1:   When you try to be your best,

To give your all and nothing less,

Many will put you to the test,

Listen to what I suggest.

Rapper 2:   Don't let others stop your progress,

Be your own person, that's success.

Don't invite failure as your guest,

To make life bitter and full of stress.

Rapper 3:   Remember the qualities you possess,

You are somebody and you are blessed.

It's not hard; it's the easiest,

Just get started, you can do the rest.

Rapper 4:   Looters, shooters and dealers don't impress

Don't let them change you, you must protest!

When it comes to deciding, you don't have to guess,

Do the right thing that's my request.

All: Life is not easy, I must confess,

But if you try, you'll find happiness,

You can do it—just be your BEST!

Name: _____

Be a Busy "Buddy"

. . . instead of a busybody

Read the paragraph and then answer the questions.

Sometimes fights continue because a third party (another person) keeps them going. People who interfere in other people's problems or arguments are called "busybodies." They like to see other people in trouble. Do not let others influence you that way. Don't let other people or your other friends talk you into keeping a fight or argument going. Once you make up, just forget your argument and remember you are friends.

Also, it is your responsibility not to become a busybody yourself. Instead, you should be a "busy buddy." A busy buddy is someone who helps others solve their problems. A busy buddy is a pal or a friend. You show responsibility when you try to be a pal or a friend to someone.

Comprehension Questions

Circle the correct answer.
1. The main idea of the paragraph is:
   a. fighting   b. interfering in other people's problems   c. a party
2. A buddy is:
   a. someone who fights   b. a pal or a friend   c. someone who has a problem

Read the following sentences. Circle *true* or *false*.
1. We should not let others influence us to keep fighting.   True   False
2. A busy buddy is a pal or friend.   True   False
3. Someone who helps people solve problems is called a busybody. True   False
4. It is my responsibility not to become a busybody.   True   False
5. We should try to make up and forget our arguments if possible. True   False

Here are some things you can say if someone tries to be a busybody in your problems.
• I am a busy buddy, not a busybody.
• I am busy helping, not busy hurting other people.
• I am his or her friend.
          Now think of some other things you could say.

Name: _____

Be a Busy "Buddy"

Fill in the missing words.

Sometimes fights continue because a _____ party keeps

them going. People who interfere in other people's problems are called

_____. They like to see other people in

_____. Do not let others _____ you to fight.

Don't let other people or your friends talk you into keeping an argument or

fight going. Once you make up just _____ your argument

and try to be friends.

Also, it is your _____ not to become a busybody

yourself. Instead, you should be a _____. A busy

buddy is someone who helps others _____ their prob-

lems. A buddy is a _____ or a _____. You should be

"busy" being a pal or friend to someone.

Word Bank

busybodies	busy buddy
third	trouble
responsibility	friend
pal	influence
forget	solve

Unit 2, Lesson 1

Name: _____

Story Starter

Responsibility

If I had a conflict with someone, I would show responsibility by . . .

_____

_____

_____

_____

_____

_____

_____

_____

_____

_____

_____

_____

_____

_____

Unit 2, Lesson 2

Name: _____

Story Starter

Respect

Write a short story about showing respect at home and at school.

_____

_____

_____

_____

_____

_____

_____

_____

_____

_____

_____

_____

_____

_____

Name: _____

Code of Conduct

I will not interrupt while you speak,

I'll wait until your sentence is complete.

I know you have feelings,

So I'll take special care.

And when we play games,

I'll play fair.

I won't be mean and make you upset,

I'll be a good friend,

I'll show RESPECT!

Name: _____

Code of Conduct

Copy the rule. Color the picture.

I will not interrupt while you speak,
I'll wait until your sentence is complete.

_____

_____

_____

_____

Name: _____

Code of Conduct

Copy the rule. Color the picture.

I know you have feelings,
So I'll take special care.
And when we play games,
I'll play fair.

_____

_____

_____

_____

_____

_____

Name: _____

Code of Conduct

Copy the rule. Color the picture.

I won't be mean and make you upset,
I'll be a good friend,
I'll show RESPECT!

_____

_____

_____

_____

_____

Unit, Lesson 2

Name: _____

Handwriting Practice

Using your best handwriting, copy your "Code of Conduct."

_____

_____

_____

_____

_____

_____

_____

_____

_____

_____

_____

_____

_____

_____

Celebrate the Difference

Choral Reading (for groups or individuals)

Group 1: I am different and that is great.

I am different, but I have no hate.

So come on everybody. Check me out.

See what I am all about.

Group 2: You are different. I think that's fine.

You are different and that's no crime.

What's on the outside is part of you,

But what's on the inside is really true.

Group 3: It's time to be friends and care for each other,

You are my sister and you are my brother.

I'll tell you no lie, and you will agree,

It's OKAY to be YOU; it's OKAY to be ME.

Group 4: If you don't get it right, you will get it wrong.

Make no mistake we ALL belong.

We are different but we think that's great.

We are different. LET'S CELEBRATE.

Research Project

The Hands

Hands convey expressions or ideas. A clenched fist is a sign of anger. A raised palm shows peace. V is for victory. Thumbs up is good, and thumbs down is bad. Pointing a finger means to blame someone for something. An encyclopedia would provide some interesting research and facts about hands. For example: There are 27 bones in the hand. Thirty-five powerful muscles move the hand. Hands can be used for good or bad. A punch is usually bad, but a handshake shows friendship and peace. It would be interesting to know how the handshake was invented and how other cultures greet each other. Look at the following three assignments. Choose one assignment. Go to the library and do the research or use the books in your classroom or home. Some information may be available on the internet. Ask for permission or help if you need it. You may do this project by yourself or as a team.

Assignments (Choose one.)

Assignment 1: Look in the encyclopedia. Report some interesting facts about hands.

Assignment 2: Look in the encyclopedia. How was the handshake first invented? What does it mean?

Assignment 3: Look in the encyclopedia. Find out how other cultures greet one another (for example: the Japanese bow).

Good Manners

I show good manners,
I say "please."

I show good manners,
I cover a sneeze.

I show good manners,
I behave in school.

I show good manners,
I follow the rules.

I show good manners,
I don't yell out.

I show good manners,
I never shout.

I show good manners,
because I know,
to show good manners
is the way to go!

Reasonable Remedies

CIA

(Conflict Intelligence Agent)

Assignment Sheet

FOR YOUR EYES ONLY!

Name: _____

Name: _____

Let's Talk

What would you say to someone you were having a conflict with? What if your friend did not want to make up? What if your friend's feelings were really hurt? What would you say? How could you become friends again? Write your answers below.

_____

_____

_____

_____

_____

_____

_____

_____

_____

_____

_____

_____

Let's Talk

Telephone Rules
for
Listening and Talking

1. I volunteer to try to work things out.

2. I will tell the whole truth.

3. I will show self-control by not yelling.

4. I will not use unkind words.

5. I want to be a good friend.

6. I will really try my best.

7. I will wait my turn before talking.

8. I know our problems can be solved if we try.

Signed by:  _____

A Is for Friendship

To have a friend, you must be a friend.
Let's look at some A-OK words for making friends.

approve

accept

acknowledge

admire

assist

What do you think these words mean? In your groups, discuss the "A" words. On the following page write down how you think each word helps us to be good friends. How many "B" words can you think of for a good friendship?

Unit 2, Lesson 3

Name: _____

Group: _____

A Is for Friendship

How do each of these words help us to be good friends?
You may use the dictionary. Write your answers below.

Approve: _____

_____

_____

Accept: _____

_____

_____

Acknowledge: _____

_____

_____

Admire: _____

_____

_____

Assist: _____

_____

_____

Think & Write—
Friendship Sayings

Pick one of the sayings below and explain it.
Write your answer on a separate piece of paper.

✽ If you see someone without a smile, give him one of yours.

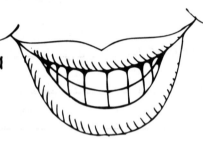

✽ Being a friend also means being a good listener.

✽ In order to have a friend, you must be a friend.

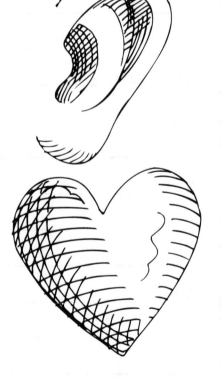

Think & Write-Master Scientist

You've invented a tonic that makes people become friends. Name your tonic (for example: Friendly Fruit Juice). Make a container for your tonic. Label it. Write a jingle about your tonic. For example:

Friendly Fruit Juice,
So good, so sweet,
It's the best,
It can't be beat!

C-A-R-E Contract

Conflicts Are Resolved Easily

When we:

* ❀ Agree to talk to each other.

* ❀ Don't say mean things.

* ❀ Tell the whole truth.

* ❀ Show you are listening.

* ❀ Don't fight.

* ❀ Try your best to solve the problem.

* ❀ Wait your turn to talk.

I agree to follow all the rules for solving my conflicts in peaceful, responsible and respectful ways.

Signed by: _____

Unit 2, Lesson 4

Special Agent: _____

Presentation

As a CIA you must make a presentation explaining the three ways to solve conflicts using good character skills. Write down what you would say about each. Then present your information to your group or to the class. You can use pictures and charts to make your presentation more interesting.

Responsibility:

Respect:

Resourceful:

CIA's Very Important Secret Business Meeting

The CIAs have a very important business meeting. Now that you are a CIA, you need to arrange the details of this meeting. Design a meeting notice, asking the other agents to attend. The purpose of the meeting is to come up with resourceful ideas to resolve conflicts. Meet with those you have invited. Once you have come up with some good ideas, submit them to

_____, the Chief CIA (your teacher).

P.S. Be sure to take your own special name tag to the meeting!

Name: _____

Special Assignment
C-A-R-E Meeting

Design your own meeting notice. Invite other CIAs. Fill in the answers to the questions using complete sentences. Use proper punctuation.

Which agents will you invite?

_____

_____

_____

What time is the meeting?

_____

Where will the meeting be held?

_____

What will you talk about concerning conflict?

_____

Nameplate

Fold on dotted line.

Draw a picture of you and your best friend on this side.

- -

My Best Friend

Name: _____

Name: _____

Think & Write-
What Have You Learned?

Read the poem "The New Kid on the Block" by Jack Prelutsky.

Have you ever had a bully give you trouble? What did you do? What could you do differently now that you've learned good character skills for resolving conflicts?

_____

_____

_____

_____

_____

_____

_____

_____

_____

_____

_____

_____

Teacher Helpers

☞ Story Starters

☞ Word Strips

☞ While You Are Waiting

☞ Folder Full of Friendly Facts

☞ Shape Book

☞ C-A-R-E Button

☞ Bookmarks

☞ Bookplate

☞ Math Helpers

☞ C-A-R-E Certificate

☞ Posters—Code of Conduct

☞ Bulletin Boards

☞ C-A-R-E Game

☞ Forms

☞ Book Log

☞ Answer Key

Making the world a better place . . .

because we care!

Story Starters

Teacher Directions

1. Make copies of the story starters on page 74. Randomly distribute the story starters to your class to get students started on homework or in-class story writing assignments.

2. Or, cut the story starters apart. Put the story starters in a bag or box. Let each student draw a card. He or she can then write the story for homework or as an in-class assignment.

3. Or, distribute copies of the same story starter and see how many different stories your class can come up with.

4. Or, play the round-robin storytelling game.

Players: Two storytellers

Object: Storytellers alternate sentences to add to the story starter. Each storyteller builds upon the last sentence of the other to create an original story.

How to Play: 1. Cut the story starters apart and put in a bag or box.

2. The first storyteller draws a card, reads the sentence out loud and completes the sentence to begin a story.

3. The second storyteller builds upon this sentence by adding his or her own.

4. Continue alternating sentences for 5-10 minutes.

Story Starters

It is okay to get angry because . . .	I try to never fight because . . .	In order to make a friend, I would . . .
When I get angry, I will . . .	I can show respect to my teacher by . . .	I can take responsibility at home by . . .
If I knew someone was lonely, I would . . .	I am special because . . .	It is okay to be different because . . .
It is wrong to be a busybody because . . .	I can show others that I care by . . .	I am a Conflict Intelligence Agent because . . .
It is not right to fight because . . .	I do not let people who fight influence me because . . .	It is good to show self-control because . . .

Tachiscope

Word Strips

Cut on the dotted lines. Insert your word strips.
See how many of your vocabulary words you know.

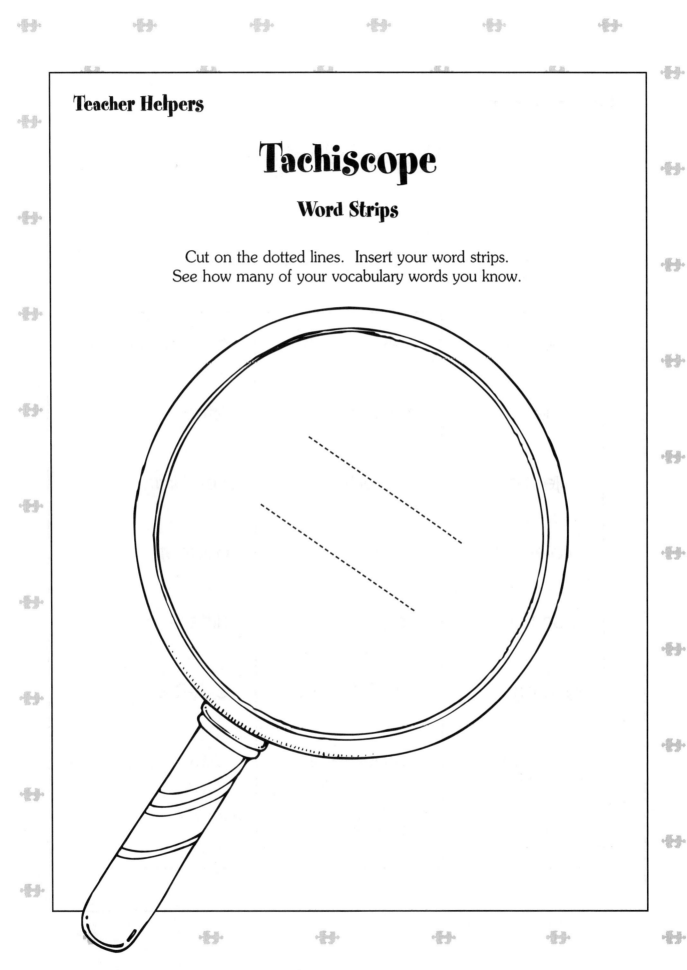

Word Strips

Tachiscope

Cut the strips apart. Using the magnifying glass tachiscope,
see how many of your vocabulary words you remember.

friendship	self-control	cooperate
rage	resolve	listen
rejection	remedy	celebrate
violence	temper	peaceful
conflict	respect	difference
revenge	responsibility	C-A-R-E
reasonable	resourceful	CIA
alone	problem	

TLC10305 Copyright © Teaching & Learning Company, Carthage, IL 62321-0010

Teacher Helpers

Name: _____

While You Are Waiting

(Extra-credit ideas or five-minute time-fillers.)

Name 10 words that say something nice or kind. (For example: beautiful)

_____

_____

_____

How many words can you make using the letters in *character*?

_____

_____

_____

Write the three Rs that cause conflicts. Then write the three Rs that solve conflicts. Can you spell them?

_____

_____

_____

Can you recite or write your "Code of Conduct" from memory? Write it on a piece of paper without looking at it.

Teacher Helpers

Folder Full of Friendly Facts

Teacher Directions: Obtain a plain file folder for each student. Let the students decorate their folders. Tell the students to fill out the papers on pages 79-80. These pages will go into their personal "Folder Full of Friendly Facts" about themselves. Let the students exchange folders with two other people. Use a timer. Each student has five minutes to review and make positive comments about the other student's folder. After five minutes, the students move on to another person's folder.

Students: Write your name on your folder. You may draw pictures or decorate the outside. Fill in the next two pages and keep them in your folder.

Teacher Helpers

Name:_____

Here are five nice words about me.

Teacher Helpers

Name: _____

Here are five of my favorite things.

My favorite game is:

_____

My favorite food is:

_____

My favorite toy is:

_____

My favorite color is:

_____

My favorite TV show is:

_____

Teacher Helpers

Name: _____

This is a picture of me.

This is a picture of *my family*.

Teacher Helpers

Name: _____

Shape Book

Teacher Directions: Fold a piece of $8\frac{1}{2}$" x 11" construction paper in half, creating a $5\frac{1}{2}$" x $8\frac{1}{2}$" cover. Fold two or three pieces of plain paper in the same way and insert between the covers. Staple along the folded edge to hold papers in place. Paste the phone pattern on the front of the book. Inside have the students write about a problem-solving conversation they might have with a friend. Hang the phones on a bulletin board or let the students share them with a classmate.

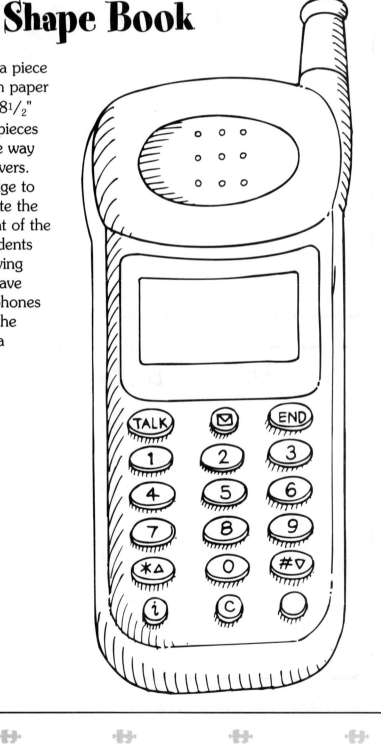

Name: _____

C-A-R-E Button

Copy onto heavy paper. Cut out the buttons.
Make a slit at the top of each. Fasten to a button on a blouse or shirt.

Name: _____

Bookmarks

Cut out the bookmarks. You may decorate and color them.

It's Not
Right

to
Fight!

In order to
have a
friend, you
must be
a friend.

Teacher Helpers

Name: _____

Bookmarks

Try Helping Instead of Hating!

Let's Talk!

Teacher Helpers

Name: _____

Bookmarks

Problems
are't
permanent.
We can work
them out!

Name: _____

Yea!
I solved my
problem
today!

Name: _____

Teacher Helpers

Name: _____

Bookplate

Cut out the bookplate. Paste or tape it inside one of your personal books.
Share your book with the class or a friend.
Remember to get permission from your parents first.

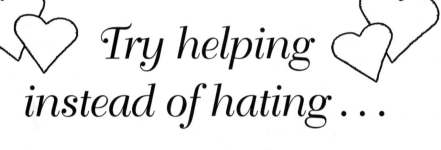

This book belongs to

_____

Name: _____

Math Helpers

1. Find someone who is having trouble with some math facts. Be a friend. Help them to study using flash cards.

2. Make up three math problems using the names of your three closest friends. Now add the name of another person who could become one of your friends. (For example: Sean has six apples. He gives them to his three friends. His friends' names are Nikki, Richard and Tony. How many apples did he give to each friend?

3. You are responsible for cleaning your room, doing the dishes and walking the dog. It usually takes you 30 minutes to clean your room, another 20 minutes to do the dishes and at least 35 minutes to walk the dog. How much time will you spend on being responsible?

4. Gloria wanted to tell her whole family about the new Code of Conduct that she learned in school. She decided to tell everyone who was coming to her family reunion this weekend. There were 30 relatives in all. She told two uncles, three aunts, six cousins, her grandfather and her little sister. How many people did Gloria talk to about respect? If she wants to talk to everyone, how many more people does she need to talk to?

Name: _____

Math Helpers

5. LaVerne invited 16 of her friends to her next CIA meeting. Seven could not come. How many friends could attend LaVerne's meeting?

6. Annette and Steve wanted to buy cookies for their classmates during the "Celebrate the Difference" party at school. They had 24 classmates in all. They bought two dozen cookies. How many cookies would each student get?

7. Annette and Steve decided they would invite two other classes to their special "Celebrate the Difference" party. The total number of students came to 72. How many packs of 24 cookies did they have to buy? How many cookies would each student get?

C-A-R-E Certificate

This is to certify that

_____

has completed the C-A-R-E Project
(Conflict And Responsibility Education)
and is an expert at solving problems
and caring for others!

Teacher: _____

Principal: _____

School: _____

Date: _____

Give each student a poster to color.

- Use the posters in your classroom to create a bulletin board or wall display.

- Post them in the hall or school cafeteria to share with other students.

- Share students' posters with other schools, preschools or local day-care centers.

- Ask students to look for pictures in magazines that illustrate the ideas in the posters and create a book or display.

Posters

- Have children write about each poster and make big books. Place in your classroom or school library.

- Ask children to work in teams to draw pictures and write verses for additional "code of conduct" posters.

Code of Conduct

I will not interrupt while you speak,
I'll wait until your sentence is complete.

Code of Conduct

I know you have feelings,
So I'll take special care.
And when we play games,
I'll play fair.

Code of Conduct

I won't be mean and make you upset,
I'll be a good friend,
I'll show RESPECT!

- Share your finished display with other classrooms or post in a central location such as cafeteria, library, lobby, etc.

Bulletin Boards

- Have students add to the display with original drawings or magazine pictures that depict the topic.

- Make additional copies of the hands or profiles and have students personalize. Place around centered posters for a unique bulletin board display.

Bulletin Boards

How to Assemble
Each Bulletin Board

✔ Reproduce the headline page.

✔ Cut out the headings or cut out individual letters.

✔ Center heading on bulletin board.

✔ Give each student a copy of the pattern to color.

✔ After the students are finished, hang their papers on the bulletin board.

✔ Optional: Make a transparency and use an overhead projector to enlarge any pattern.

✔ Optional: Allow your visual learners to help design your bulletin board.

There's no doubt

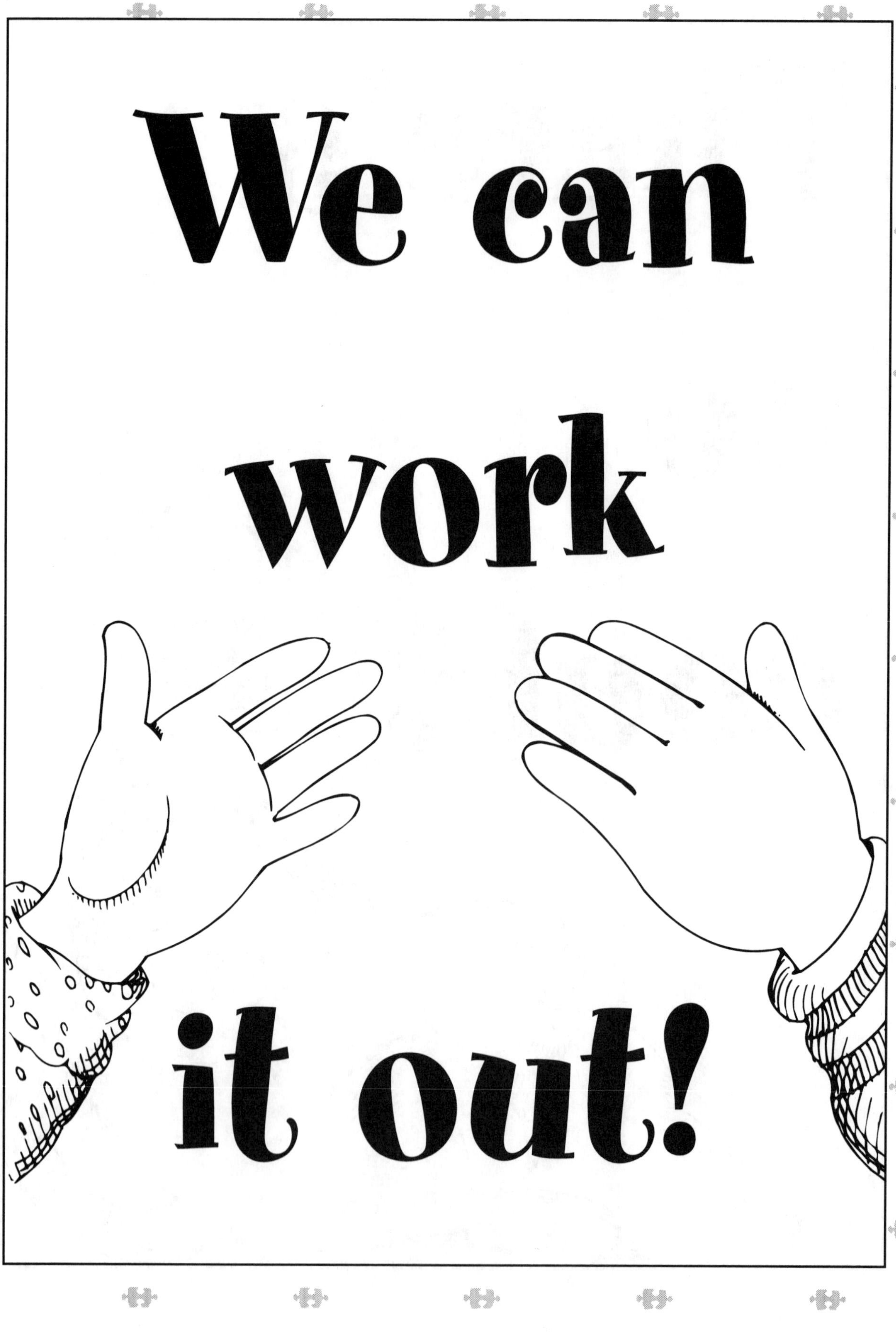
We can
work
it out!

Use with Story Starters on page 74.

C-A-R-E

(Conflicts Are Resolved Easily)

GAME

C-A-R-E

(Conflicts Are Resolved Easily)

Directions

- The object of the game is to show how you have learned to solve problems by using good character skills.
- Two CIAs can play.
- Each agent chooses a token and places it on Start.
- Mix up the Question Cards and place them facedown on the Draw Pile space.
- One agent draws a card and reads the question to the other agent. The other agent then answers the question. If the answer is correct, he or she may move forward as directed on the card. If the answer is incorrect, he or she may not move.
- The agents take turns reading the questions to each other and moving forward.
- If directions are written on the space that an agent lands on, the player must follow the directions.
- The first CIA to eliminate harmful conflict wins. An agent can get to the end with the exact number or a larger number.

Teacher

1. Cut the game apart.
2. Mount the gameboard on the inside of a file folder.
3. Mount the directions on the front of the folder.
4. Laminate the folder if desired.
5. Laminate the playing cards and tokens and place them in a locking plastic bag inside the folder.
6. Store in a file or a manila envelope.

Game Pieces

Cut apart and store in a zip-type bag.

You were angry, but you did not fight. You may move ahead 3 spaces.	A conflict is a disagreement between two or more people. Answer: yes Move 2 spaces.	The word resolve means "to bring something to a successful end." Answer: yes Move 2 spaces.
The three Rs that make conflicts turn to violence are: rage, revenge and rejection. Answer: yes Move 4 spaces.	You did not interrupt when someone was talking. You may move ahead 3 spaces.	Are conflicts normal? Answer: yes Move 2 spaces.
Two ways to handle conflicts are to show responsibility and respect. What is the third way? Answer: Be resourceful in finding solutions. Move 4 spaces.	The word rage means "to be very upset and out of control." Answer: yes Move 2 spaces.	What does it mean to feel rejected? Give an example. Answer: It means to feel left out or unwanted.
You did not take revenge on someone. Your teacher is proud of you. Move 4 spaces.	You apologized when you made a mistake or hurt someone's feelings. Move 3 spaces.	What do you have to do to have a friend? Answer: You must be a friend. Move 3 spaces.
What are people called who interfere in other people's problems and make them worse? Answer: They are busybodies. Move 2 spaces.	Should you dislike someone because they are different from you? Answer: No. Because we are all special and important. Move 2 spaces.	What does the word CIA stand for? Answer: Conflict Intelligence Agent Move 2 spaces.
True or False? Reasonable remedies are similar to compromises? Answer: true Move 3 spaces.	Name the three Rs of good character. Answer: respect, responsibility, resourceful Move 3 spaces.	You showed good manners at home, in your classroom, and in the lunchroom. You may move 3 spaces.

2 dozen Cookies

You lost
your self-control.

Go back
3 spaces.

You remembered
your good
manners.

Go forward
2 spaces.

You listened to a
busybody and got
into trouble.

Go back
2 spaces.

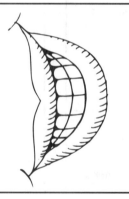

C-A-R-E

(Conflicts Are Resolved Easily)

Start

Finish

I CARE!

You did
not share.

Go back
1 space.

104

You helped some-
one else today.

Go forward
3 spaces.

You are a good
friend.

Move forward
3 spaces.

Draw Pile

You forgot to say,
"please."

Go back
1 space.

Discard Pile

You showed
respect to your
teachers.

Move forward
3 spaces.

Forms

The C-A-R-E Project Grade Sheet (optional)

Grade Level: _____   **Room No.** _____

Name	Unit 1			Unit 2			Final
1.							
2.							
3.							
4.							
5.							
6.							
7.							
8.							
9.							
10.							
11.							
12.							
13.							
14.							
15.							
16.							
17.							
18.							
19.							
20.							

Give two or three grades per unit.

The C-A-R-E Project Special Homework or Project
Assignment Sheet   Grade Level: _____   Room No. _____

Name of Student	Name of Project/Homework	Date	Due	Grade

Student/Parent Conference Form
The C-A-R-E Project

While teaching *The C-A-R-E Project*, you may want to plan student conferences. This is a good post-assessment tool for this curriculum. These conferences may be conducted with just the student or with the student's parents. Here are some things you may want to discuss.

What have you learned so far about conflict?

What still bothers you about conflict?

What else would you like to learn about conflicts?

What else can you do to show you are responsible?

Unit Evaluation Form for Teachers

After each unit, you may want to do a brief evaluation. Your notes will help you prepare for future lessons.

Name of Unit: _____

	Excellent	Good	Fair	Needs Improvement
How would you rate the goals and objectives for this unit?				
How would you rate students' responses to the lessons?				
How would you rate the overall quality of the unit?				
What do you think about the writing activities?				

What should be added to the unit?

What did you think was particularly good about the unit?

What would you change about the unit the next time you teach it?

What are your other comments and thoughts?

Book Log

Books About Conflict Management, Anger Management and Character Education

There are many wonderful books about conflict and responsibility. To keep up, use this handy log and add any books you hear about. Later you can purchase them or find them in the library.

Author	Title	Year	Grade Level
Aborn, Allyson	*Everything I Do You Blame on Me: A Book to Help Children Control Their Anger* Publisher: The Center for Applied Psychology	1994	Elementary
Holden, Dr. Gerri	*Students Against Violence* Publisher: Teacher Created Materials	1995	Elementary
Lachner, Dorothea	*Andrew's Angry Words* Publisher: North-South Books, New York	1995	Elementary
Prelutsky, Jack	*The New Kid on the Block* Publisher: Greenwillow	1984	Elementary
Shapiro, Lawrence E.	*Sometimes I Like to Fight, but I Don't Do It Much Anymore: A Self-Esteem Book for Children with Difficulty in Controlling Their Anger* Publisher: The Center for Applied Psychology	1995	Elementary
Viorst, Judith	*Alexander and the Terrible, Horrible, No Good, Very Bad Day* Publisher: Aladdin Paperbacks	1987	Elementary

Answer Key

ABC Order, page 26
1. conflict
2. problem
3. resolve
4. violence

Word Scramble, page 29
1. conflict
2. resolve
3. violence
4. problem

ABC Order, page 32
1. alone
2. rage
3. rejection
4. revenge
5. self-control
6. temper

ABC Order, page 37
1. alone
2. conflict
3. problem
4. rage
5. rejection
6. resolve
7. revenge
8. self-control
9. temper
10. violence

Word Search, page 39

```
N  S  P  R  O  B  L  E  M
R  E  J  E  C  T  I  O  N
E  L  O  V  E  F  R  Q  T
S  F  A  E  O  I  V  S  L
O  C  O  N  F  L  I  C  T
L  O  R  G  E  R  O  N  E
V  N  A  E  K  A  L  U  M
E  T  G  A  N  G  E  R  P
N  R  A  G  E  R  N  E  E
D  O  R  E  J  E  C  B  R
A  L  O  N  E  E  E  S  T
```

Missing Vowels, page 40
1. violence
2. conflict
3. rage
4. problem
5. temper
6. resolve
7. rejection
8. revenge
9. alone
10. self-control

Vocabulary Search (Test), page 41
1. e
2. d
3. b
4. g
5. a
6. c
7. f

Comprehension Questions, page 47
1. b.
2. b.

1. true
2. true
3. false
4. true
5. true

Be a Busy "Buddy," page 48

Sometimes fights continue because a **third** party keeps them going. People who interfere in other people's problems are called **busybodies**. They like to see other people in **trouble**. Do not let others **influence** you to fight. Don't let other people or your friends talk you into keeping an argument or fight going. Once you make up just **forget** your argument and try to be friends.

Also, it is your **responsibility** not to become a busybody yourself. Instead, you should be a **busy buddy**. A busy buddy is someone who helps others **solve** their problems. A buddy is a **pal** or a **friend**. You should be "busy" being a pal or friend to someone.